FAMILY DYNAMICS

Embrace Your Sound

by Courtney Vowell Woodward

illustrated by Thu Vu

Four Hearts

To Preston & Lyla
May you always be proud of who you are.
PS – Love you the most!

An imprint of Four Hearts Books

www.courtneywoodward.com

ISBN 979-8-9854607-1-1 Hardcover
ISBN 979-8-9854607-0-4 Paperback

Violin lived in a local music store.
She had been there all her life and never
ventured away from her family of instruments:
THE STRING FAMILY.

Every day, Violin heard enchanting music coming from other parts of the store.

But no matter what she tried, she couldn't make the same incredible sounds.

One day, a little girl picked Violin up...

...and didn't put her back.

Bells jingled against the store's front door.
The store owner, Ms. Marilynne, closed early and
didn't notice that Violin had been misplaced.
Music still played in the distance.

As Violin swiftly snuck to the back, she bumped into a family of instruments.
"Hi there, we're
THE WOODWIND FAMILY."

"Hi!" Violin bounced with glee.
"I wish I could sound like you.
I've tried, but I can't.
See?"

Flute then introduced
Clarinet, Oboe, and Bassoon.
They also needed air to make a sound,
but had reeds made of cane.
Violin was surprised at how different they all were.
Their sounds were different too.

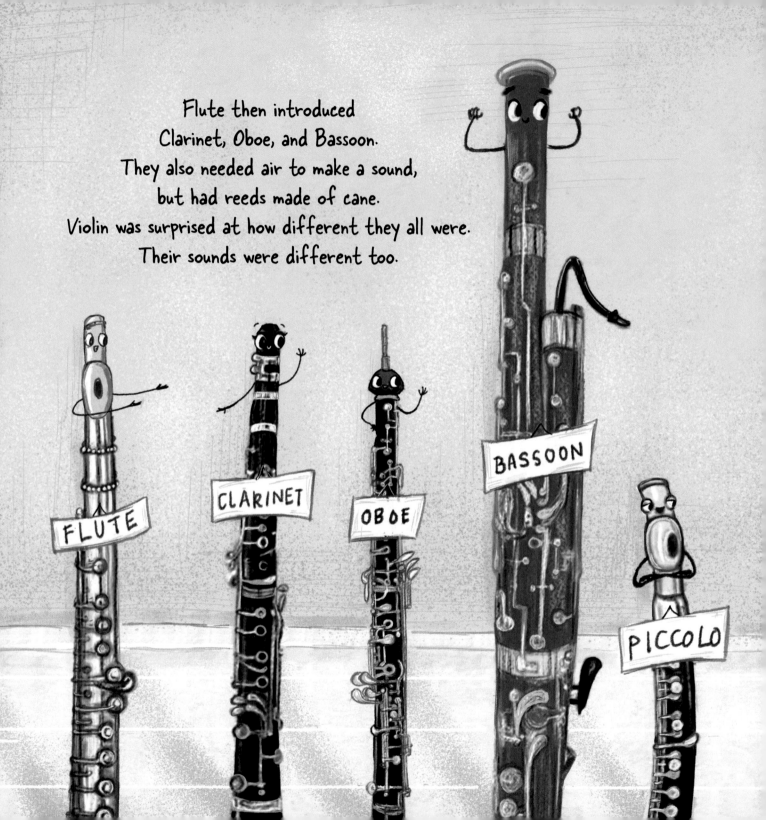

Suddenly, Violin heard a very low voice and curiosity struck.
She dashed around the next corner so fast, she forgot to say goodbye.

"Helloooooooo!"

the voice bellowed.

BRASS FAMILY

Violin felt a little nervous, but before she could say anything, a cheerful instrument twirled toward her.

"I don't need air to make a sound,
I have a bow and strings," Violin said sadly.

"I wish I could sound like you."

Violin quickly noticed one particular brass instrument.
"Wait, you don't have valves at all!" she gasped, wide-eyed in wonderment.

SLIDE

TROMBONE

"You're right, Violin.
I'm Trombone and I have a slide.
I still need air to make a sound,
but my slide helps me change pitch."

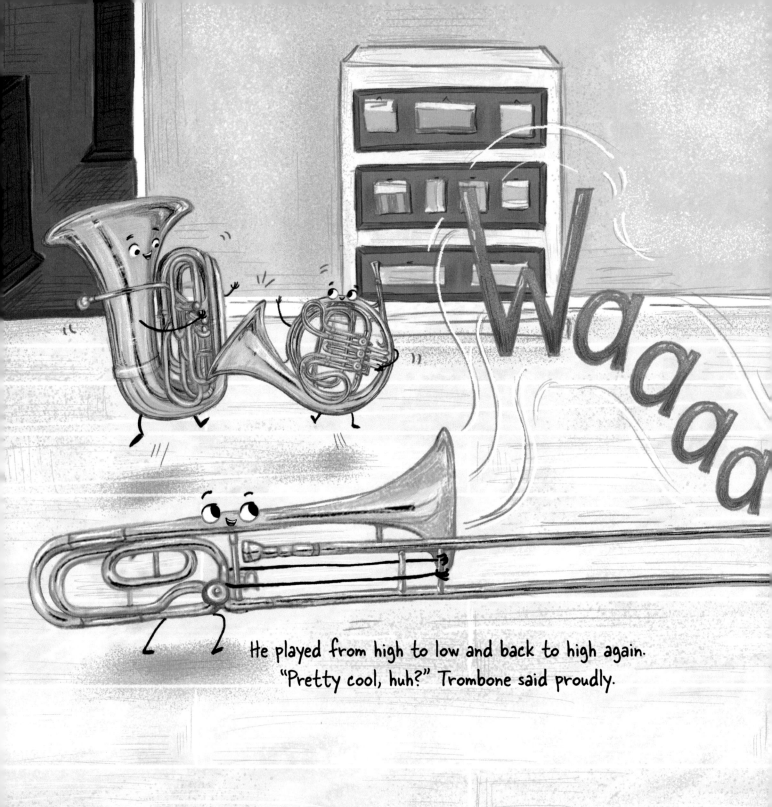

He played from high to low and back to high again.
"Pretty cool, huh?" Trombone said proudly.

But Violin was already around the next corner, hoping to see more instruments!

Next, she found
THE PERCUSSION FAMILY.
Violin's eyes grew wide. "Your family is so BIG!"
Tambourine responded: "Oh, there are *many* more," as he pointed behind him.

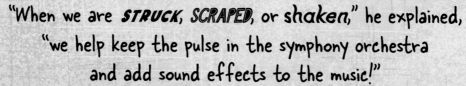

"When we are **STRUCK**, **SCRAPED**, or shaken," he explained,
"we help keep the pulse in the symphony orchestra
and add sound effects to the music!"

"I *definitely* don't sound like you,"
Violin responded, hanging her head.

"If you head to the way, way back, I bet you'd sound more like Ms. Grand Piano," said Snare Drum, hoping to cheer Violin up.

"Thanks." Violin waved goodbye and went on her way.

At the back of the store, she found a grand piano
with *STRINGS* inside!

MS. GRAND PIANO

"Hello, little one. You seem to be in a hurry. Where are you headed?"
Ms. Grand Piano said sweetly in a southern drawl.

"I always hear pretty music in the store,
but can never sound quite like the other instruments.
You have strings like me. Can I sound like you?" Violin asked hopefully.

Ms. Grand Piano responded: "I do have strings,
but I have keys too – 88 to be exact!
When my keys are pressed, a hammer inside hits my strings to
make a sound. So, I'm part of two families,
PERCUSSION *and* **STRINGS.**"

"Oh. I don't have any keys..." Violin felt discouraged.

Bells jingled against the store's front door.

Violin neared her section and stopped suddenly in her tracks.
There, in front of her, were all four instrument families
in perfectly rounded arcs, playing together.

As Violin stepped closer to the full ensemble, she could hear all of the instruments' voices from high to low and everything in between. Whether they had strings, valves, a slide, or made fun sound effects, all of the instruments blended together beautifully, creating enchanting, colorful sounds.

Violin was able to hear the true beauty
of different instruments all performing as one.

Violin caught a glimpse of her family.
They were smiling, waving, and pointing to
an empty seat right at the front!

Violin sat down beaming with pride as she looked at her family and her new friends.

Violin looked up with a
CRESCENDO OF CONFIDENCE,
her bow in playing position.

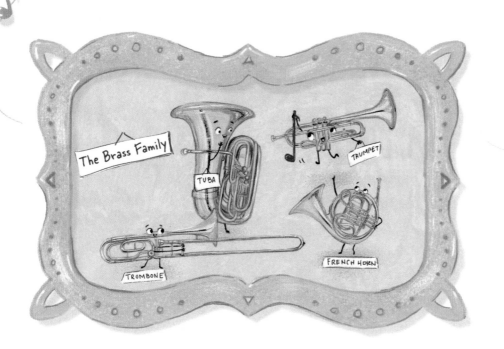

The Brass Family

TUBA

TRUMPET

TROMBONE

FRENCH HORN

The Percussion Family

MARIMBA

SNARE DRUM

BASS DRUM

TAMBOURINE

CYMBALS

The Percussion & String Family

MS. GRAND PIANO

About the Author

COURTNEY VOWELL WOODWARD

Music Education with Heart

Courtney Vowell Woodward is a wife, mom, former music educator, business owner, and author.
After teaching music education in the classroom for 15 years, Courtney now hopes to share her passion for music through early children's literature. Wanting to introduce a love of music in every family's home, Courtney incorporates basic musical knowledge inside heartfelt stories — stories that include long-lasting life lessons.

Her classroom not only focused on upper-level musical skills, but on family, fun, and inclusion — themes that you will also see reflected in her writing.

Courtney hopes that music education will become an easily accessible, essential subject for students of all ages!

Scan the QR code to receive the free coloring pages you see above!